PENGUIN BOOKS

NEVER GIVE UP

Jacky Fleming went to a suffragette school in London. She emerged awesomely uneducated due to the teachers' inexplicable preference for Latin as a first language. A year at Chelsea School of Art and a degree in Fine Art at Leeds University greatly improved her table-football technique. Other qualifications include A– for posture and a silver medal in Latin-American dancing. A brief stint in the art department of a London periodical was followed by eleven years' teaching art as a foreign language. Jacky lives in Yorkshire and still hates cooking.

Her cartoons have been published by the BBC, The Women's Press, Virago, Leeds Postcards, Aberdeen University Press, Longman, *Spare Rib*, The Open University and others. Penguin also publishes her popular first book of cartoons, *Be a Bloody Train Driver*.

JACKY FLEMING

never give up

PENGUIN BOOKS

PENGUIN BOOKS

Published by the Penguin Group
Penguin Books Ltd, 27 Wrights Lane, London W8 5TZ, England
Penguin Books USA Inc., 375 Hudson Street, New York, New York 10014, USA
Penguin Books Australia Ltd, Ringwood, Victoria, Australia
Penguin Books Canada Ltd, 10 Alcorn Avenue, Toronto, Ontario, Canada M4V 3B2
Penguin Books (NZ) Ltd, 182–190 Wairau Road, Auckland 10, New Zealand

Penguin Books Ltd, Registered Offices: Harmondsworth, Middlesex, England

First published in book form 1992
3 5 7 9 10 8 6 4 2

Printed in England by Clays Ltd, St Ives plc

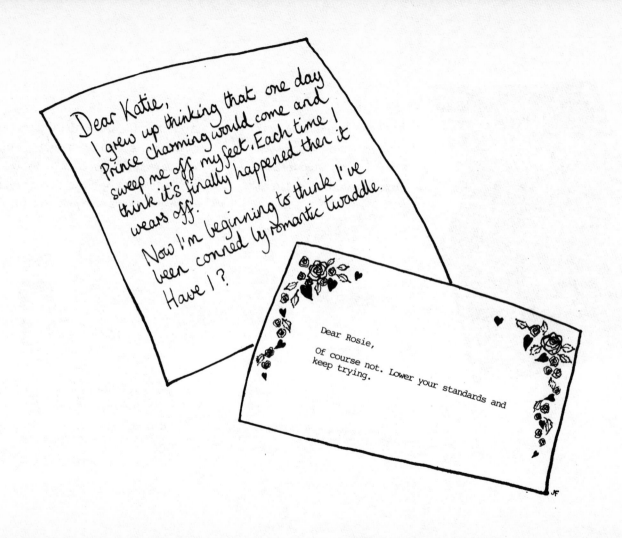

Dear Katie,
I grew up thinking that one day Prince Charming would come and sweep me off my feet. Each time I think it's finally happened then it wears off.

Now I'm beginning to think I've been conned by romantic twaddle.

Have I?

Dear Rosie,

Of course not. Lower your standards and keep trying.

FANNY
and
JOHNNY

or

ANYTHING IS
BETTER THAN
BEING single

Fanny is a waitress.
Because she has to WORK
for a living she doesn't
look as good as she could

AUDIENCE WONDER IF THEY LOOK AS
MISERABLE AS SHE DOES

Everyone in the café is very nice
considering they are single, lonely
and depressed. They even make a
birthday cake for one of their regulars
which just makes everyone feel worse.

INCLUDING THE AUDIENCE

Fanny lives with a gay man. Does this mean she's AVOIDING something? Is there something about heterosexual men she can't HANDLE?

It certainly looks that way

Meanwhile back at the cafe one of the older waitresses is rushed to hospital and dies. This is a direct result of being single.

are we going to end up like her?

PANIC RIPPLES THROUGH THE AUDIENCE

Illness and death can only be avoided one way...

Meet Johnny, just out of jail and lonely as HELL. He wants Fanny but she doesn't want him. Which is odd because he's fairly handsome and she IS single.

Luckily for Fanny, Johnny won't take no for an answer and pesters her relentlessly.

Clearly the woman is a bit nicked

Johnny recognizes this as DEFENSIVE behaviour and nothing personal.

Finally we discover why Fanny's
been acting so STRANGELY.
Her last partner used to beat
her up.

Fanny's neurotic defenses crumble
and they can finally look forward
to a lifetime of domestic bliss

They curl up together
and sleep like spoons

THIS IS NOT ONE OF THOSE NASTY FILMS ABOUT
SEX AND THE SINGLE WOMAN

Not forgetting the OTHERS who are
still out there, single and lonely.

The End

AUDIENCE LEAVES CHASTENED, FULLY PREPARED
TO MARRY ANYONE WITH A PULSE

...and they lived happily ever after until the birth of their first child when he went to pieces and she went off sex entirely.

women have finally realised there is
only one source of true happiness

chocolate mousse

Little boys see mummy as
HUGE and all powerful

this image never
entirely fades

In order to become men they must
BREAK AWAY from mummy

I'm leaving home.
Can you make my sandwiches?

this pattern also never changes

As it was never his job to look after mummy, he never does

this makes women 'demanding'

But it IS mummy's job to look after him

this means men don't need to be demanding

Girls, on the other hand, never need to break away from mummy because

they will never have to look after themselves...

just everyone else.

It's best to learn this early on. JF

it's NOT post natal depression

PMT SURVIVAL KIT IV

CHRONIC DANGER TIME as you are not yet aware that you have PMT

CHRONIC DANGER TIME as you are not yet aware that you have PMT

CHRONIC DANGER TIME as you are not yet aware that you have PMT

self adhesive diary stickers

THIS MAY LOOK LIKE MY USUAL UNREASONABLENESS **IT ISN'T.** PMT

DO YOURSELF A FAVOUR and GIVE ME A WIDE BERTH

PMT   PMT

and some useful badges

ON NO ACCOUNT ALLOW ME TO DISCUSS **SEPARATION** THIS WEEK We can discuss it next week

AVOID ANY UNNECESSARY CONVERSATION ONLY ASK QUESTIONS WHICH REQUIRE YES/NO ANSWERS LEAVE AGAIN PROMPTLY

JF

PMT SURVIVAL KIT V

Home alone

Living alone is so peaceful you could hear a pin drop

that wasn't a pin

Living alone means you can have the whole bed to yourself

and feel in complete control of your life

but you can get a taste for it

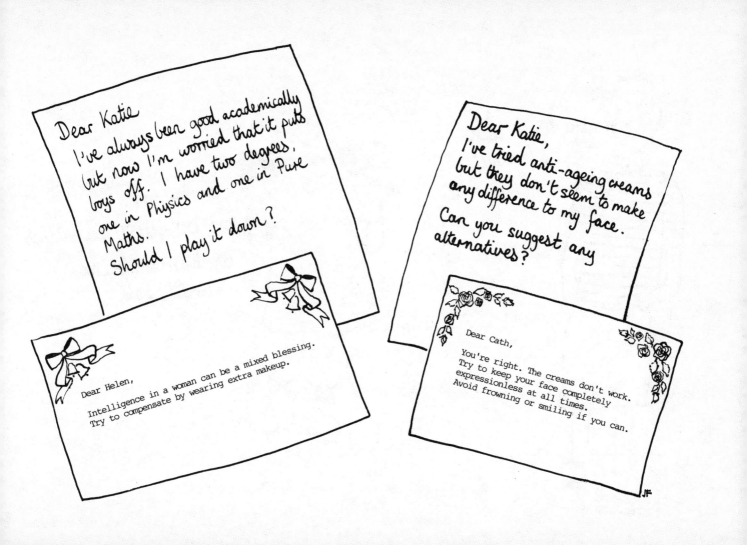

Dear Katie
I've always been good academically but now I'm worried that it puts boys off. I have two degrees, one in Physics and one in Pure Maths.
Should I play it down?

Dear Helen,

Intelligence in a woman can be a mixed blessing. Try to compensate by wearing extra makeup.

Dear Katie,
I've tried anti-ageing creams but they don't seem to make any difference to my face.
Can you suggest any alternatives?

Dear Cath,

You're right. The creams don't work. Try to keep your face completely expressionless at all times. Avoid frowning or smiling if you can.

you don't look
like a feminist

WATCH OUT –
we DISGUISE ourselves
as human beings
until DUSK

JF

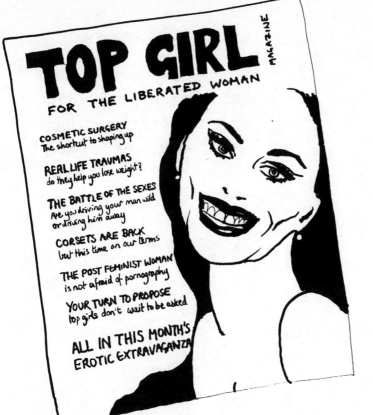

and when we're feeling REALLY liberated we even punch ourselves in the face!

Close up

Stand in front of the mirror
and take a GOOD look.
What do you see?

Let's take a closer look.
Have you been neglecting
your knees and elbows?

me isn't it?

I do believe
I HAVE

Is your bottom crying out
for an exfoliating scrub?

Have your breasts begun
their slow descent?

Take a closer look at your feet.
When did you last PAMPER them?

When did I
last LOOK
at them

And when did you last take a
SERIOUS look at your back?

not WHEN
but HOW?

Is your stomach trim and flat, or has the winter bulge got the better of you?

oh PLEASE
Winter, spring, summer AND autumn

Here are fifty tips to get you looking good

take it or leave it, I say

JF

I found this fabulous little
man who just moved my
buttocks round to the front.
So simple.

if I were thinner

I'd be thinner

Donald you look a prat

REAL chic is
always ahead of
its time

I'll wear what I like

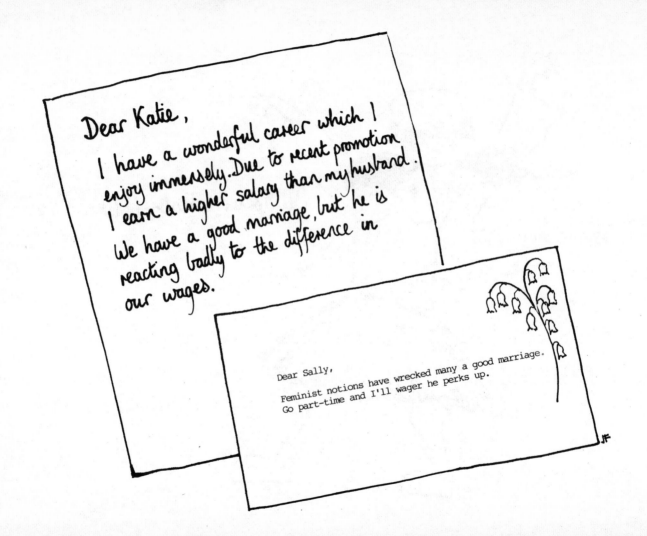

Dear Katie,

I have a wonderful career which I enjoy immensely. Due to recent promotion I earn a higher salary than my husband. We have a good marriage, but he is reacting badly to the difference in our wages.

Dear Sally,

Feminist notions have wrecked many a good marriage. Go part-time and I'll wager he perks up.

'Droves of burnt out, infertile, unfulfilled women are leaving their careers and returning home, cheated of love and children by the hollow promises of feminism'

Teaching is its own reward

no I wouldn't rather be a housewife
I'd rather have good pay good job opportunities
childcare facilities justice decent contraception
abortion on demand safe streets comfortable
clothes less of your lip and a bit of RESPECT.
And a whisky.

JF

Dear Katie,

Sometimes my husband gets drunk and becomes aggressive. Last week he kicked the cat. Most of the time he's an easy going sort of man.

Am I doing something to upset him?

Dear Janice,

Probably. Perhaps you've been wearing a colour he doesn't like. Try to find out what he does like and keep to it.
Some men are very sensitive.

JF

If he was so VIOLENT towards her I fail to comprehend why she didn't merely LEAVE him. I myself have a little pied à terre in St James's which I frequent when occasion demands

the suggestion that we're out of touch
is preposterous. I have even travelled
on the underground, I think

He seems a thoroughly decent fellow to me, who has obligingly provided regular beatings to a remarkably ungrateful wife

There are of course many reasons why DEFINING rape is not a simple process — had she perhaps been pleasant towards him, was she attractively clothed, had she consented on PREVIOUS occasions, had she been breastfeeding in his presence...

...did she say NO in such a way that it could be understood as YES, did she fight him off in a manner which could have implied consent?

All these things make it very DIFFICULT for a man to understand the messages he's being given

All things bright and beautiful
except for all women
All creatures great and small
except for all women
All things wise and wonderful
except for all women
The Lord God made them all
although how He could make such a blunder
I will never be able to fathom unless it was
to do the cleaning

JF